DILBERT®

Gives You the Business

A DILBERT® BOOK

BY SCOTT ADAMS

**Andrews McMeel
Publishing**

Kansas City

For Pam, The Queen of Lists

Other DILBERT books from Andrews McMeel Publishing

Don't Step in the Leadership
Journey to Cubeville
I'm Not Anti-Business, I'm Anti-Idiot
Seven Years of Highly Defective People
Casual Day Has Gone Too Far
Fugitive from the Cubicle Police
Still Pumped from Using the Mouse
It's Obvious You Won't Survive by Your Wits Alone
Bring Me the Head of Willy the Mailboy!
Shave the Whales
Dogbert's Clues for the Clueless
Build a Better Life by Stealing Office Supplies
Always Postpone Meetings with Time-Wasting Morons

For ordering information, call 1-800-642-6480.

DILBERT® is a registered trademark of United Feature Syndicate, Inc.

DOGBERT and DILBERT appear in the comic strip DILBERT®, distributed by United Feature Syndicate, Inc.

www.dilbert.com

ISBN: 0-7407-4071-7

If you're a typical *Dilbert* reader, the question in your mind right now is, "How can I use this book as a weapon to embarrass my enemies?"

I realize that's a gross generalization. The more noble-minded *Dilbert* readers are thinking, "How can I use this book as a weapon to embarrass my friends?" Still others are wondering how they can steal this book from their friends and call it "borrowing."

But whether you have friends or not, I'm here to help.

Responding to an avalanche of suggestions, I have gathered all the most-requested *Dilbert* strips about the business world and organized them by topic. If you want to find all the best *Dilbert* comics on, for example, budgeting, or programming, or performance reviews, or engineering, or marketing, they're here, along with dozens of other topics.

This is a huge improvement over the old method where you might have access to only one or two *Dilbert* comics to make your point. It's nearly impossible to do a thorough job of mocking someone when you are so limited in your choice of comics. Thanks to this book, that will never be a problem again. Now you can show someone a few dozen *Dilbert* strips on the same topic and be certain your message gets across. You'll never again have to deal with the same annoying question, "Are you trying to tell me something?"

It wasn't easy to pull this book together. I stayed up all night, with comics spread around on my furniture and the floor, sorting them into categories. My cat, Sarah, helped by rolling around in the piles until the static electricity made the strips stick to her fur. It wasn't much help, but I don't pay her much either. If you find any duplicates or strips out of place, blame my cat. If the whole book is missing, your friends probably "borrowed" it.

Speaking of friends, you might want to join Dogbert's New Ruling Class and rule by his side when he conquers the planet and makes everyone else our domestic servants. Joining is as easy as signing up for the free *Dilbert* newsletter, published about four times a year whenever I feel like it.

To subscribe, send a blank E-mail to dilbert-text-on@list.unitedmedia.com.
To unsubscribe, send a blank E-mail to dilbert-off@list.unitedmedia.com.
If you have problems with the automated subscription write to newsletter@unitedmedia.com.

You can also subscribe via snail mail:
    Dilbert Mailing List
    United Media
    200 Madison Ave.
    New York, NY 10016

S. Adams

Scott Adams

Jobs ———————————————————

Job Impediments ———————————————

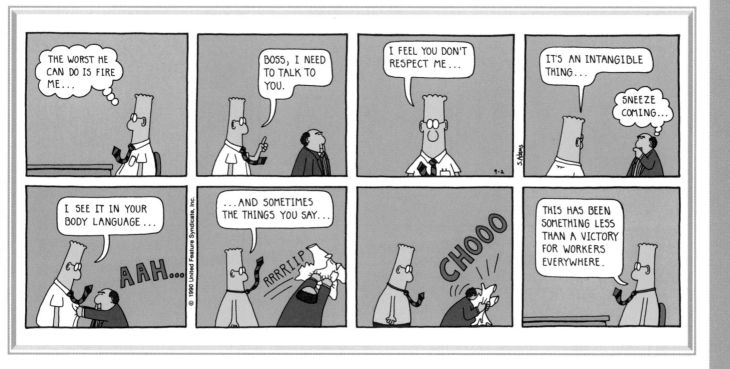

BOSSES

BOSSES

BOSSES

BOSSES

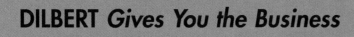

BUDGETING AND ACCOUNTING

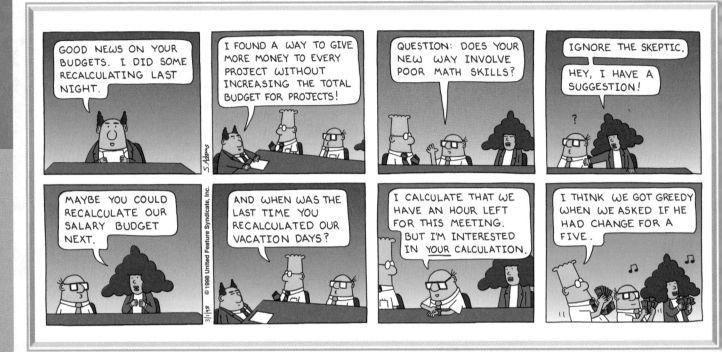

Panel 1: ALTHOUGH YOUR COMPANY IS VERY PROFITABLE, I WOULDN'T BE MUCH OF A CONSULTANT IF I DIDN'T RECOMMEND CHANGES.

Panel 2: YOU RECOMMEND JAILING OUR OMBUDSMAN AND DECLARING MARTIAL LAW... MAKES SENSE.

Panel 3: THEN COULD I SHOOT EMPLOYEES WHO MAKE PERSONAL PHONE CALLS?
IT'S OKAY WITH ME.

Panel 4: AS A CONSULTANT, I'M OVERPAID EVEN IF I DO BAD WORK.

Panel 5: WHEREAS YOU'RE UNDERPAID EVEN IF YOU DO GOOD WORK.
IT'S FUNNY IF YOU THINK ABOUT IT.

Panel 6: I MIGHT HAVE A TERRIBLE JOB, BUT AT LEAST I DON'T HAVE ANY JOB SECURITY.

Panel 7: I CAN MAKE YOUR EMPLOYEES MORE CREATIVE AND SPIRITUALLY FULFILLED.

Panel 8: I USE MY SPECIAL BLEND OF POETRY AND DANCE TO TOUCH THEIR SOULS.
OKAY. YOU'RE HIRED.

Panel 9: THERE ONCE WAS A DOG WITH A HAT... WHO GOT PAID TO DANCE LIKE THAT...
HEY! MY SOUL JUST HEALED!

Panel 10: HAVE MY POEMS AND DANCES HEALED YOUR SOUL YET, ALICE? THE COMPANY CARES ABOUT YOUR TOTAL WELL BEING.
EXCUSE ME.

Panel 11: WE WANT MORE MONEY, NOT MORE DANCING DOGS!!! M-O-N-E-Y!!

Panel 12: SO YOU'RE SAYING THOSE PRIMAL SCREAMS ARE HEALTHY? CAN YOU TEACH ME TO DO IT?
HERE'S MY INVOICE—GO WILD.

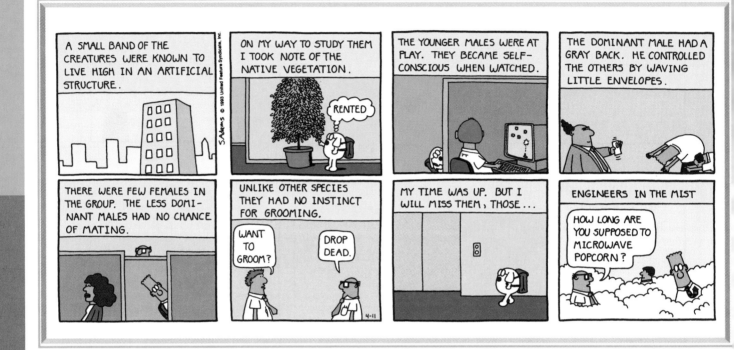

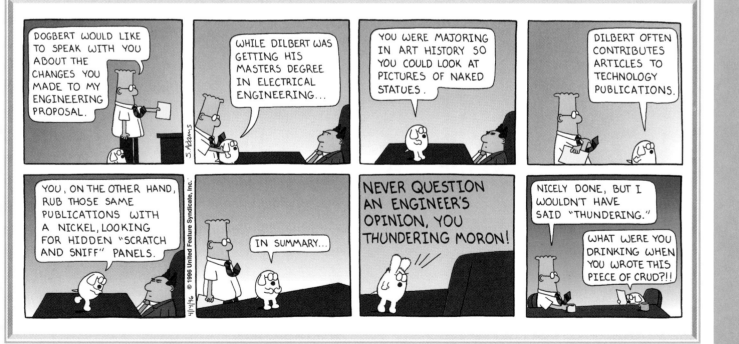

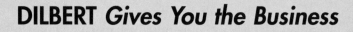

Strip 1:

CATBERT: EVIL H.R. DIRECTOR

MY EYES ARE SORE FROM USING THE COMPUTER.

TRY TYPING WITH YOUR FINGERS, THE WAY EVERYONE ELSE DOES.

PERSONALLY, I FIND COMPUTERS VERY RESTFUL ON MY EYES.

Strip 2:

CATBERT: H.R. DIRECTOR

WHEN YOU DUMPED MORE WORK ON WALLY, DID HE MOAN? OR DID HE SCREAM?

IT SOUNDED LIKE THIS... AAOO-MUW AAHH-OW-OW!!

THE STAFFING LEVELS SOUND ABOUT RIGHT.

Strip 3:

CATBERT: EVIL H.R. DIRECTOR

I'M NOT ENJOYING MY JOB.

TAKE THIS POWERFUL ANTI-DEPRESSANT DRUG FOR THE REST OF YOUR LIFE.

I DIDN'T KNOW H.R. COULD PRESCRIBE DRUGS.

I'D HATE TO LIVE IN A WORLD WHERE THAT WAS ILLEGAL.

"BOSS-PROOF CAP."

Strip 4:

CATBERT: EVIL H.R. DIRECTOR

THE COMPANY'S GOAL IS TO DOUBLE THE EFFICIENCY OF ALL EMPLOYEES.

QUESTION: IF WE DOUBLE OUR EFFICIENCY, WON'T YOU DOWNSIZE HALF OF US?

DON'T TALK TO ANYONE IN MARKETING; THEY AREN'T SO GOOD AT MATH.

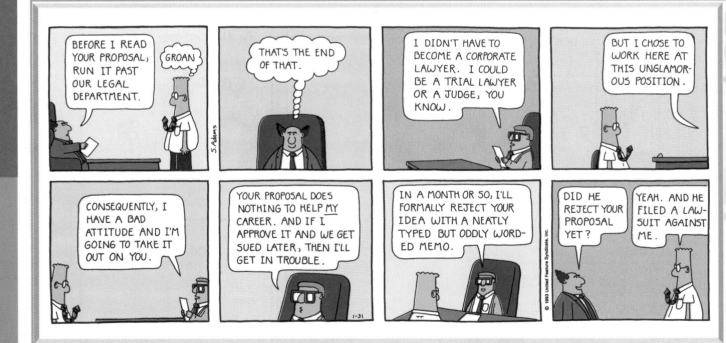

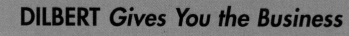

MARKETING

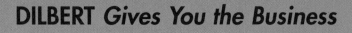

PROJECT MANAGEMENT

PROJECT MANAGEMENT

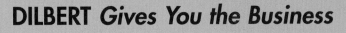

PROJECT MANAGEMENT

RETAIL AND SERVICE JOBS

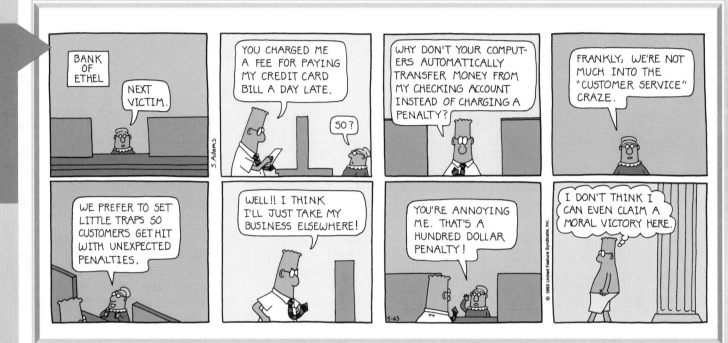

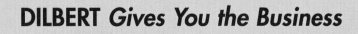

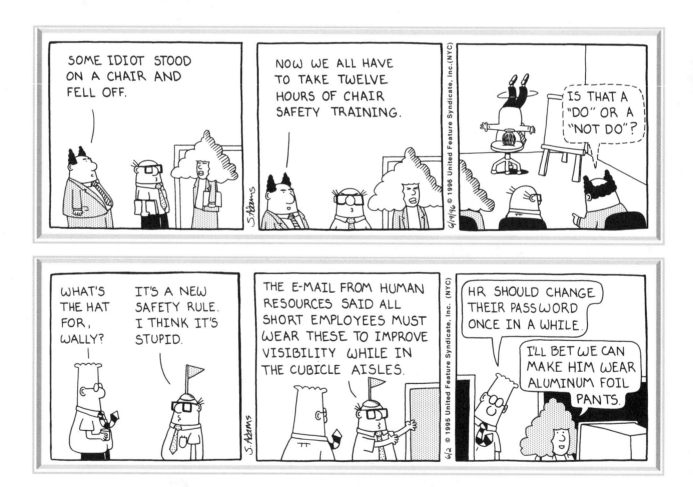

SALES

IT LOOKS LIKE SALES OF THE "DOGBERT JOGGEROBIC CARPET PATCH" ARE BRISK.

YEAH, AND I'M LOOKING TO EXPAND.

RATBERT IS BUSY RESEARCHING NEW PRODUCT CONCEPTS FOR THE CARPET PATCH.

"CARPET CLUB FOR MEN."

DILBERT, YOU'RE BEING TEMPORARILY TRANSFERRED TO THE FIELD SALES ORGANIZATION.

NORMALLY WE USE THESE ASSIGNMENTS TO ROUND SOMEBODY OUT FOR MANAGEMENT. BUT IN THIS CASE I'M JUST YANKING YOUR CHAIN!

YOU'RE OVER-COMMUNICATING AGAIN, SIR.

PLUS, I HATE THE MANAGER OF SALES.

SO... DILBERT, WELCOME TO THE SALES DEPARTMENT. I'M TINA, YOUR NEW BOSS.

HI

AS THE NEW GUY, YOU GET THE CUSTOMERS WHO DESPISE OUR PRODUCTS AND WANT TO HURT US PERSONALLY.

I HATE YOU! I HATE YOU!

YOU'LL BE SELLING TO THE SMALL BUSINESS MARKET. HE'S YOUR BEST ACCOUNT.

WELCOME TO SALES TRAINING.

AS YOU KNOW, OUR COMPANY MAKES OVER-PRICED, INFERIOR PRODUCTS. WE TRY TO COMPENSATE BY SETTING HIGH SALES QUOTAS.

WE DON'T ASK YOU TO ACT ILLEGALLY, BUT IT'S PRETTY MUCH THE ONLY WAY TO REACH QUOTA. OKAY, THAT'S IT FOR TRAINING. ANY QUESTIONS?

DILBERT *Gives You the Business*

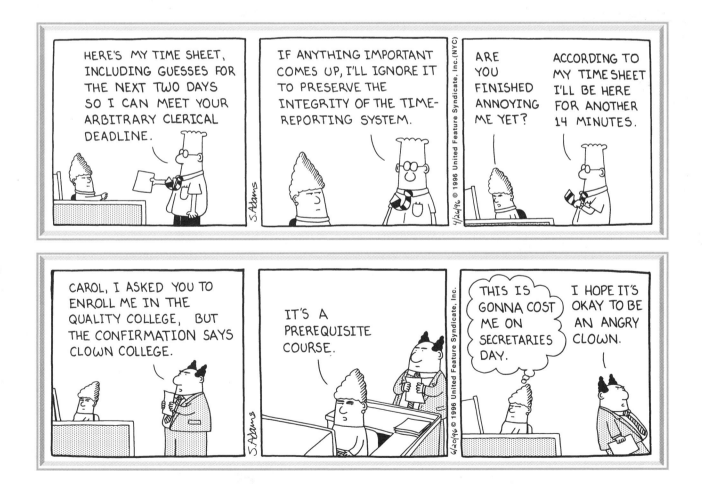

DILBERT *Gives You the Business*

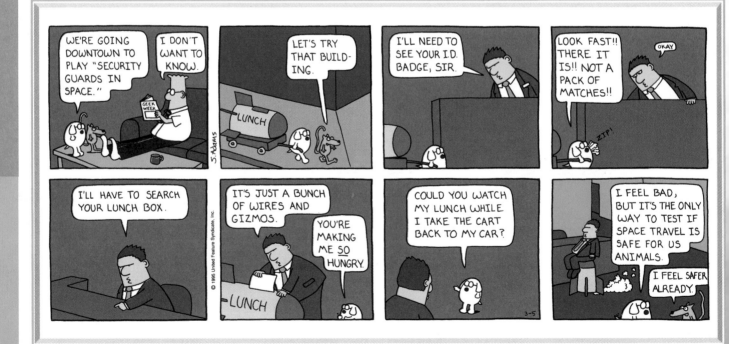

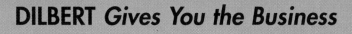

TRAINING

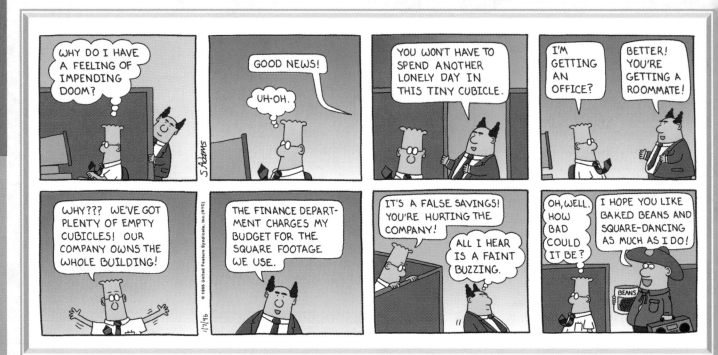

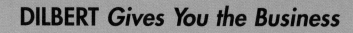

ANNOYING
CO-WORKERS

BUSINESS LANGUAGE

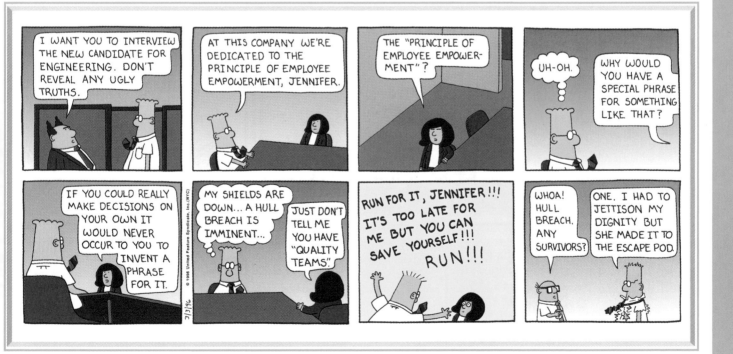

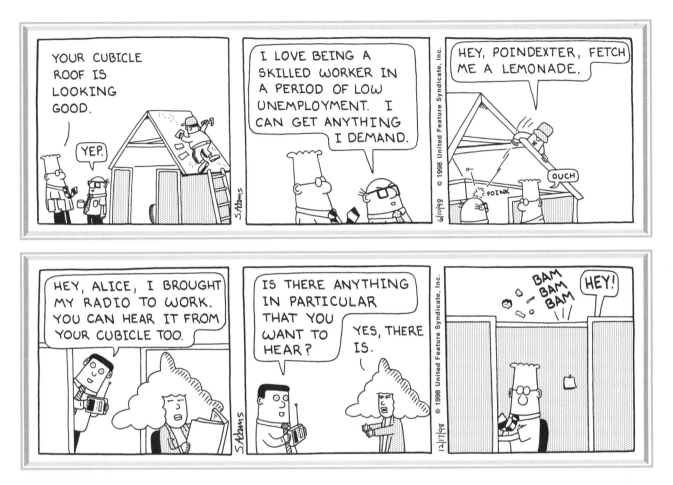

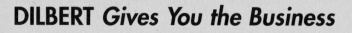

INCENTIVES

MEETINGS AND PRESENTATIONS

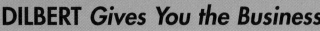

DILBERT *Gives You the Business*

THEY SAY PEOPLE FEAR PUBLIC SPEAKING MORE THAN THEY FEAR DEATH.

SO TECHNICALLY, IF YOU KILL A GUY WHO'S SCHEDULED TO SPEAK, YOU'RE DOING HIM A FAVOR.

WHEN ARE YOU GOING TO SLEEP?

NEVER.

DOGBERT THE C.E.O.

I'M AN INVESTMENT BANKER. I CAN HELP YOU LOOT THIS PLACE AND ESCAPE.

YOU'LL MERGE WITH MY OTHER CLIENT COMPANY. YOUR GOLDEN PARACHUTE KICKS IN. THEN YOU EXERCISE YOUR STOCK OPTIONS ON THE UPTICK.

YOU RARELY SEE A MERGER ANNOUNCEMENT WITH THE PHRASE, "SO LONG, SUCKERS."

OUCH.

THE COMPANY ANNOUNCED WE'RE BEING BOUGHT BY OUR LONG-TIME RIVAL.

DON'T WORRY ABOUT LAYOFFS. THEY LIKE ENGINEERS. IN FACT, THEY ALREADY HAVE A DIVISION THAT DOES WHAT WE DO!

EXCEPT THEY'RE YOUNGER AND THEY AREN'T PAID AS MUCH AS WE ARE...

SPIN

AFTER THE MERGER, WE'LL REDUCE STAFF IN AREAS THAT ARE REDUNDANT.

I HOPE THE EMPLOYEES OF THIS COMPANY WILL BE EVALUATED FAIRLY COMPARED TO THOSE IN THE BUYING COMPANY.

WE ALREADY HAVE A BALD GUY.

DOES YOURS STEAL OFFICE FURNITURE, TOO?

MERGERS

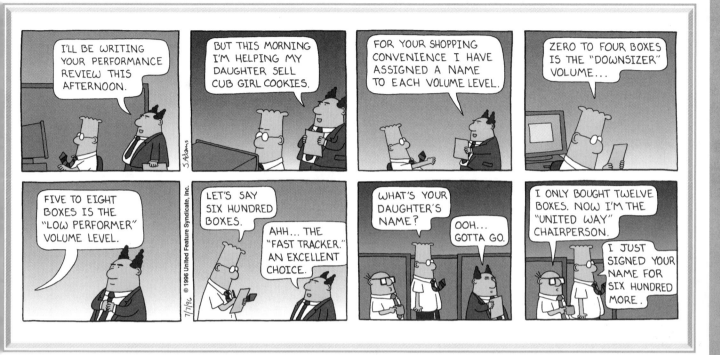

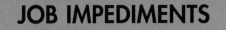